FAIRY DOLL'S HOUSE

STICKER BOOK

igloobooks

I'm Fairy Petal and this is my pretty toadstool doll's house, made for me by my fairy friends. Can you help me finish the rooms by finding each missing item on the sticker sheets?

LAUNDRY ROOM

The laundry room is missing lots of items, most importantly a washing machine! What other stickers can you add?

PRETTY KITCHEN

This is the doll's house kitchen. It should have lots of things to help bake tasty treats. Can you find them on your sticker sheets?

GARDEN ROOM

The fairy garden room is warm and welcoming, but can you help me make it even better by adding some stickers?

SPELL ROOM

This room is where all my dolls make sparkly spells. Can you help me find the items for an extra-special spell?

Pretty Kitchen
pages 4-5
Spell Room
pages 8-9

Beautiful Bedroom
pages 10-11
Garden Room
pages 6-7

Flower Garden
pages 14-15
Fairy Bathroom
pages 12-13

Laundry Room
page 3
Extra Fairy Stickers
Here are some extra fairy stickers, just for you!

BEAUTIFUL BEDROOM

Every doll needs a pretty bedroom.
Help me make it even more beautiful
by adding all of the missing things.

FAIRY BATHROOM

No fairy bathroom would be complete without a special bathtub. Can you help me find it? There are lots of bottles missing, too!

FLOWER GARDEN

The flower garden is a lovely place to relax and play, but lots of things are missing. Look for them on your sticker sheets.

FAIRY FINDING GAME

Now that you have decorated my doll's house, I have a game for you! There are six special items to find in this book. Once you've found them, write the page number under each picture.

Answers: item a = page 14, item b = page 4, item c = page 9, item d = page 11, item e = page 12, item f = page 6.